GH00864904

My L
Purple Book

First steps in Bible reading

Jo Bailey

© Scripture Union 2003
First published 2003
ISBN 1 85999 720 1

Scripture Union, 207–209 Queensway, Bletchley, Milton Keynes, MK2 2EB,
England
Email: info@scriptureunion.org.uk
Website: www.scriptureunion.org.uk

Scripture Union Australia
Locked Bag 2, Central Coast Business Centre, NSW 2252
Website: www.su.org.au

Scripture Union USA
P.O. Box 987, Valley Forge, PA 19482
Website: www.scriptureunion.org

The right of Joanna Bailey to be identified as author of this work has been asserted by her in
accordance with the Copyright, Designs and Patents Act 1988.

Scripture quotations are from the Contemporary English Version © American Bible Society
1991, 1992, 1995. Anglicisation © British & Foreign Bible Society 1996. Used with permission.

British Library Cataloguing in Publication Data.

A catalogue record of this book is available from the British Library.

Illustrations: Jenny Tulip at Beehive Illustration Agency
Cover and internal design: Mark Carpenter Design Consultants
Additional material: Maggie Barfield, Val Mullally (page 63)
"One hundred sheep" (page 10) reprinted from *Let's Join in!* © SU 1990 op.
"Thank you, Lord" (page 34) reprinted from *One hundred and one ideas for creative prayers*,
SU, © Judith Merrell 1995, and used with permission.

Typesetting: Servis Filmsetting Ltd, Manchester
Printed and bound by Interprint Limited, Malta

Scripture Union is an international Christian charity working with churches in more
than 130 countries providing resources to bring the good news about Jesus Christ to children,
young people and families – and to encourage them to develop spiritually through the Bible
and prayer.

As well as a network of volunteers, staff and associates who run holidays, church-based
events and school Christian groups, Scripture Union produces a wide range of publications
and supports those who use the resources through training programmes.

What's in this book?

How to use this book

When children are small, before they can read, it can be hard to know how to introduce the Bible to them. The *Tiddlywinks Little Books* offer a simple and enjoyable way to do so. Each book introduces Bible stories and truths through the lives of young children today. As they explore and discover and learn about the Bible in their day-to-day lives, they share their discoveries with us. There isn't a "right" way to use *Tiddlywinks Little Books*. If you'd like to read something every day, each numbered page gives you a story and a prayer idea. Alternatively, you could read several pages in one go for a longer story. *Little Books* do not tie you to a certain date: use them as often as suits you and your child. Young children enjoy hearing stories again and again, so don't feel you have to keep moving on or can only read a section once. There are extra pages too with ideas for activities, rhymes and crafts, and things for the children to do themselves. Plus a page for you, as you seek to introduce ideas about God and the words of the Bible to the children in your care.

You might like to set aside a time for using the *Little Books*, perhaps at bedtime or while you have a meal together. Or keep the book handy so you can use it anytime – on a bus journey, at a pause in a day of busy playing or while you're waiting for a visitor to call.

Children in their early years are growing faster and learning more than at any other time in their lives – an ideal time to take their "First steps in Bible reading".

Note to parents and carers: the biblical story of Jairus' daughter (Mark 5:21–43) makes it clear that the young girl had died, but the version on pages 11 and 12 of this book does not say that explicitly. You may wish to alter the wording for your own children if you feel they are ready to think and talk about death with you.

Meet Lily

This is Lily. She is nearly four years old. Her house is always noisy as she has two older sisters, called Li-Ling and Li-Lian, and an older brother called Kai-Loong. They also have a big dog called Sam. Lily likes having lots of people around, but sometimes she gets fed up with being the youngest. When she feels left out, she plays ball with Sam.

Lily loves dressing up. Her friend Krista lives next door and they often dress up as princesses. The girls have just started ballet lessons where they wear pink leotards. Lily's mum has just bought Lily her first pair of ballet shoes and she can't wait to wear them. When she grows up, Lily wants to be a police officer, like her dad. Kai-Loong says you can't do ballet *and* be in the police, but Lily says she's going to do *both*! Four mornings a week Lily goes to pre-school. On Sundays Lily and her family go to church.

Lily enjoys being with her friends and hearing stories about Jesus. Her grandad (Lily calls him Gung Gung) and grandma (Por Por) live in Hong Kong, which is a long way away. They saw Lily when she was a baby but she was too young to remember that. They often write to Lily and sometimes she speaks to them on the phone.

What do you think Lily tells them about? Let's find out…

"Hello! I'm Tiddly Ted!
Look for me as you share this book!"

Lily feels left out

Lily's house was noisy as usual. Her brother and sisters all had friends round to play. Lily wanted to play too but they had shut themselves away in their bedrooms. Even Lily's mum was busy cooking tea in the kitchen. Lily was feeling left out. Do you ever feel like that?

Jesus was often busy too. One day some mothers brought their children to see Jesus. Jesus' helpers said, "Jesus doesn't have time for your children. Please take them away."

Jesus heard what they said. He was sad that they thought he was too busy. He said,

"Please don't send them away. Bring the children to me."

The children came to Jesus. He hugged them and put his hands on their heads. He told them that God loves children.

And if God loves children, that means he loves you too!

Pray

Thank you, Jesus, that you love me and that I'm special and important to you.

Luke 18:15–17

A big hug for Lily

Lily was feeling grumpy. Why wouldn't anyone play with her? Kai-Loong was playing football with his friend in the garden. Li-Lian and Li-Ling were upstairs with their friends, playing music and dancing. "I don't care, I'll go and play with Sam!" Lily cried. But Sam was asleep in his basket and he didn't want to play.

Lily found her mum in the kitchen, "Mum, what can I do? Will you play with me?"

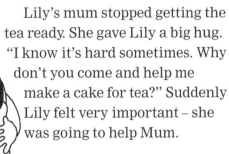

Lily's mum stopped getting the tea ready. She gave Lily a big hug. "I know it's hard sometimes. Why don't you come and help me make a cake for tea?" Suddenly Lily felt very important – she was going to help Mum.

Jesus told his friends, "Children are very important. They know how to love God. You should be like them and love God too."

Pray

Tell God about someone who makes you feel important.

Luke 18:15–17

Sam gets lost. . .

"Sam! Come here!" Lily's mum was shouting really loudly!

Sam isn't always good at coming when he's called. Today in the park Sam spotted a squirrel. He chased after it, running and running, right out of sight. Sam didn't come back.

In the end, Mum and Lily had to go home without him. Lily cried. Later, Lily's dad went to the park to look for Sam. At last they both came back home. Sam was looking very sorry for himself!

Lily remembered a story that Jesus told about a sheep getting lost. The shepherd was very worried. He loved all his sheep. He went out to look for the missing sheep. He looked and searched until he found it. He carried his sheep all the way back home. He was so pleased to have found his sheep that he had a party to celebrate!

Pray

Think about something that you lost and then found again. Tell God how you felt.

Lily loses her mum

Lily and her mum were in the supermarket. As they walked down the aisles, Lily spotted some shelves of toys. She skipped over to have a look. "Mum, can I have one of these dolls for my birthday?" Lily asked. But Mum didn't answer. She wasn't there! Where was she? Lily looked all around her. She began to cry. Just then her mum came rushing round the corner.

"There you are!" Mum sounded very relieved. "I'm glad I've found you!"

That night Lily said thank you to God that her mum found her. Lily said, "Now I know how the lost sheep felt. He would have been pleased to see the shepherd!"

Mum said, "I think I know how the shepherd felt! Jesus is like a shepherd. He takes care of us like a shepherd takes care of his sheep."

Pray

Thank you, Jesus, that you love me and care for me.

Luke 15:1–7

One hundred sheep

Here's an action rhyme to say and do about the lost sheep.

One hundred sheep I had with me,
(Spread arms wide, then point to self.)
But one has gone astray.
(Point into the distance.)
Where, oh where can that sheep be?
(Shrug shoulders.)
I must find her today.
(Shield eyes.)
Everywhere I seemed to look,
(Look all around.)
By river, hill and tree,
*(Ripple fingers, make an arch for hill,
spread arms above head.)*
Then I saw her by the brook –
(Point and smile.)
Happy, happy me!
(Point to self.)

Lily visits the doctor

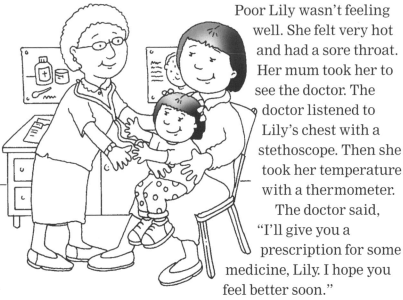

Poor Lily wasn't feeling well. She felt very hot and had a sore throat. Her mum took her to see the doctor. The doctor listened to Lily's chest with a stethoscope. Then she took her temperature with a thermometer.

The doctor said, "I'll give you a prescription for some medicine, Lily. I hope you feel better soon."

People who were ill often came to see Jesus. There weren't many doctors around. People knew Jesus would help them.

When Jairus' daughter was ill, he too rushed to find Jesus. "My little girl is very sick," he said. "I don't think she will ever get better. Please come." Jesus set off for Jairus' house.

When Jesus arrived, he did make her better – her dad was very surprised! And very pleased. Find out more about what Jesus did on the next page.

Pray

Thank you, Jesus, for doctors and nurses who help people when they are ill.

Mark 5:21–43   11

Lily feels better

Lily was playing at doctors. She set out all her teddies and dolls around the room. She got out her doctor's set. She listened to all their chests with her stethoscope. She put bandages on them. "There you are everyone. Aren't you lucky to have such a great doctor looking after you?" Lily said.

Jairus was glad that Jesus was coming to see his daughter. When they were nearly there, some men rushed up and said, "It's too late! Your daughter will not get better."

But Jesus said, "Don't be scared. She will get well."

At Jairus' house, everyone was sad. "Why are you crying?" Jesus asked. "The little girl is just asleep."

Jesus went inside. "Little girl, get up!" he said. And she did!

"Now she is hungry," smiled Jesus. "Give her something to eat."

Everyone was amazed at Jesus. He had made the little girl well again.

Pray

Do you know anyone who is not well? Ask God to help them.

Mark 5:21–43

Police officer Dad

Lily thinks her dad looks smart in his police uniform. She likes to hear stories about what he does at work. "Today I found a lady who had been robbed. Someone took her bag. I managed to catch the robber and get her bag back."

Jesus tells a story about a man who was robbed and hurt as he

was travelling along a lonely road. The poor man was left lying on the road. He needed help. A man walked along, but he hurried past. Another came walking along. But he didn't stop. Then along came a kind man from another country. He *did* stop. He cleaned the man's cuts and put on some bandages. He put the man on his donkey and took him to a safe place.

"That's just like my dad when he helps people," Lily thought.

Pray

Thank you, God, for police officers and for other people who help us.

Luke 10:25–37   13

Lily helps Sally

Lily was talking to Krista. "When I grow up I'm going to be a police officer, and help people just like my dad. Mum told me that Jesus wants us to be kind and help people when we can."

That day at ballet there was a new little girl in their class, called Sally. She looked a bit different. She was wearing an old T-shirt and shorts, not a pretty ballet dress like Lily's. Sally didn't want her mum to go and she started crying. Lily wanted to stand near Krista, but then she remembered the story

Jesus had told about the kind traveller. He had helped the man who was in trouble.

Lily said, "Come on Krista, let's go and make friends with Sally."

Sally stopped crying and gave a little smile when Lily told her they would be her friends.

Pray

Dear Jesus, please help me to be kind to people I meet.

Luke 10:25–37

Down on the farm

Mum had brought Lily and Krista to a farm. They had bought some bags of food to feed the animals. Can you see which animals they are feeding now? Lily and Krista thought the pigs

looked funny, rolling around in the mud.

Jesus told a story about a man who looked after pigs. But that wasn't what he *wanted* to do . . .

He was fed up with working on his dad's farm. So he left home and went far away. He had lots of parties and made lots of friends. But soon he had spent all his money and everyone left him. He was all alone. He needed a job. All he could do was look after the pigs. He was so hungry he even wanted to eat the pigs' food! He felt very miserable and lonely.

Pray

Dear God, please help all the people in the world who feel sad and lonely.

Lily feels sorry

Li-Ling was at school. She had been colouring a picture. Lily really wanted to try her new jumbo colouring pens. She used them on Li-Ling's picture. But the picture didn't look as good when she'd finished. Lily knew Li-Ling would be upset. She told Mum, "I've drawn on Li-Ling's picture."

Mum sighed. "When Li-Ling gets home, you must tell her how sorry you are!" she explained.

Do you remember the son who left home? He was very sorry. He knew he'd made his father sad. "I'm going to go home and see if my dad will forgive me," he said. He thought his dad would be cross.

When he was still a long way from home, his father ran to meet him and gave him a big hug. He had been waiting so long for his son to come home.

Pray

Can you think of anything you do that makes people sad? Tell God that you're sorry.

Luke 15:11–32

Help the son go home

Party time!

"Mum, is it my birthday party today?" Lily was so excited. She was nearly four. She'd been planning her party for ages. Mum had bought the toys for the party bags and had prepared all the food. Lily had invited Lucy and Liam and some of her other friends from pre-school, and of course Krista was going to be there. They were going to play pass the parcel and musical bumps. Lily couldn't wait!

When his son came home, the father in Jesus' story planned a party. He was so happy to have his son home again. He wanted to celebrate. He dressed his son up in beautiful clothes and shoes. He invited all

their friends and neighbours and prepared plenty of food. It was a great party!

Pray

Do you like going to parties? Say thank you to God for the fun that you can have at parties.

Luke 15:11–32

On the roof

"I've had a busy day today," Lily's dad said. "I had to climb up a ladder and rescue a cat from a roof – he couldn't get down!"

Four men wanted to see Jesus and they ended up on a roof! Their friend couldn't walk. They carried him on a mat to see Jesus. There were so many people in the house where Jesus was that they couldn't even get through the door. They had to think of something! The house was very different from our houses – it had a flat roof

with steps on the outside, not the inside. So the four men could carry their friend up the outside stairs and onto the roof. They made a hole in the roof. Then they lowered their friend through the hole into the room below. Imagine how surprised everyone was!

Pray

How can you help your friends?
"Please God, help me to help my friends when I can."

Luke 5:17–26

Poor Lily

Lily has fallen over in the playground at pre-school. "Ouch! My knee is bleeding!" she cries.

Krista runs over. "Are you all right?" she asks.

Krista helps Lily up and takes her to one of the helpers. They go indoors and put on a bandage.

Lily is glad she has friends to help her.

The four men were worried about their friend. They had lowered him down through the roof. Jesus looked up and saw how much they wanted their friend to get better. They had tried so hard to get him into the house. Jesus said to the man, "God knows that you are sorry for the wrong things you have done. Get up! Pick up your mat and walk home!" At once the man jumped up. He could walk! Everyone was amazed and said thank you to God.

Pray

How do your friends help you?
"Thank you God for my special friends."

Luke 5:17–26

Down through the roof

The four men have brought their friend to see Jesus. Can you draw the man on the mat?

Up the tree!

Do you like climbing? Liam does. He and his sister Lucy were playing with Lily. Liam is full of energy. When he saw the climbing frame in the garden, he started to climb it straight away, right to the top. "I can see for ever!" he laughed.

"Come down, now," called Lily's mum.

"I'm stuck!" Liam shouted. Mum climbed up and rescued Liam. He was a bit quieter after that!

One day, Jesus met a man who'd done some climbing – he'd climbed a tree! Zacchaeus wanted to see Jesus. But so did lots of other people. Zacchaeus was only little and he couldn't see over the crowd. So he climbed a tree for a good view. Jesus saw Zacchaeus sitting on the branches. Jesus called up, "Come down Zacchaeus! I want to come and visit you at your house."

Pray

Thank you, God, for the times when friends come to play.

    Luke 19:1–10

No friends?

Lily was moaning. "Mum, Sarah at pre-school is really naughty. She keeps taking toys off everyone. No one likes her."

Lily's mum said, "Maybe she's lonely. It can't be much fun for Sarah, not having any friends. You could try asking if she wants to play with you."

"No way!" said Lily. "She's not my friend. I'll just play with Krista!"

No one liked Zacchaeus either. He was a cheat and he stole money. When Jesus asked to eat with him everyone was shocked. "Why is Jesus going there?" they moaned. "Doesn't Jesus know what Zacchaeus is like?"

Jesus didn't listen.

Zacchaeus hurried down from the tree, leaves and twigs going everywhere. He was delighted that Jesus was coming to his house.

Pray

Thank you, Jesus, that you want to be friends with everyone.

Friends!

Sarah was sitting on her own at pre-school. She was looking a bit sad. Lily remembered that her mum had suggested being friendly to her. Lily went over.

"Do you want to come and play with the doll's house?" Lily asked.

Sarah looked a bit surprised, but slowly nodded her head. They played together until milk time.

Later Lily told her mum, "Sarah was all right really. She shared her biscuit with me!"

Do you think Zacchaeus was glad to have Jesus as a friend? After their meal together, Zacchaeus said something surprising to Jesus. He stood up and said, "I have been mean. But now I want to do right. I will give half of my things to the poor and I will pay back everyone I cheated!" Zacchaeus had really changed after his time with Jesus!

Pray

Help me to be kind to people who don't have many friends.

Luke 19:1–10

Everyone is hungry!

"I'm not sharing my picnic!" shouted Lily. Krista sniffed and tried not to cry.

"Poor Krista is hungry," Mum said.

"She can have a sandwich," muttered Lily, "but I'm having the crisps."

"It would be much kinder to share everything," Lily's mum pointed out.

There are some hungry people in today's story from the Bible. Jesus and his friends crossed a big lake in a boat. On the other side, a big crowd of people were waiting for them. They wanted to hear about God. Jesus started teaching them and telling them stories. After a while Jesus said, "Everyone's getting hungry. Where can we get food to feed all these people?"

Jesus' friends moaned, "We don't have enough money to buy food for all of them!"

What do you think will happen next?

Pray

Sorry, God, for the times when I'm not very good at sharing.

A boy's lunch

Everyone had loved listening to Jesus, hearing the stories he told and the wonderful things he said about God. But it was late and they were getting hungry. Jesus' friends were worried. They asked, "Where can we get food for all these people?"

One little boy gave his lunch to Jesus. It wasn't very much food – just five small loaves of bread and two fish. It wouldn't be enough to feed all those people . . .

Unless . . .

Jesus did something amazing!

What do you think he did?

Lily looked at her picnic. She loved crisps, but Mum was right. It would be much kinder to share all her food. She and Krista shared everything out. And they both enjoyed their picnic more!

"I even had enough to eat," Lily thought as they ran to play on the swings together.

Pray

Please help me to be good at sharing even when it's hard.

     John 6:1–13

Food for all

Jo at church was telling the story of the big picnic. "Lots of people were listening to Jesus. They were hungry. One boy had his lunch with him – five loaves of bread and two fish. He gave his picnic to Jesus. Jesus asked everyone to sit down. He said thank you to God and then started passing round the bread and the fish. I'm sure Jesus' friends didn't think there would be enough to feed everyone."

"Was there enough?" Lily wanted to know.

"Plenty. There was even some left over. Jesus had surprised his friends again!"

Jo went on, "There are lots of children in the world who don't have enough food. I wonder if we could help them."

The children all decided they would like to. Can you think of some ways they might help?

Pray

Please help me to think of ways to help children in our world who don't have enough to eat.

John 6:1–13

One stormy night. . .

It was a dark and stormy night. The wind was whistling in the
trees. Lily couldn't get to sleep. She was scared. She crept
downstairs to see Mum and Dad. She whispered, "I'm
frightened."

Dad put his arm around her and said, "Once Jesus' friends
were frightened too.
They were in a boat,
sailing across a lake
when a big storm
blew up. Jesus was
asleep in the boat. He
was tired. The wind
grew louder, the waves
grew bigger. Water
splashed into the boat.
The boat started
sinking.

"The friends shook Jesus awake. 'We're going to drown!'
they cried.

"Jesus got up and said 'Wind and waves be quiet!' The
storm stopped. Everything was calm. 'Why were you so afraid
when I was with you?' Jesus asked them."

Pray

Dear God, when I am scared, help me to
remember that you are with me.

Luke 8:22–25

After the storm

The day after the storm, Lily's family were taking Sam for a walk in the park. There was a man checking the rowing boats on the lake. All the rain from the night before had filled the boats and he was bailing out the water. Lily grabbed her dad's arm. "In the story you told me last night, the water came crashing into Jesus' boat. His friends were really scared until Jesus told the wind to stop!"

"That's right," said Dad. "And what happened when Jesus said that?"

"It worked!" shouted Lily. "The storm stopped. Just like that! And they were all safe."

"That must have been amazing," said Mum. "Only Jesus could do that. We couldn't stop a storm!"

"I think being with Jesus must have been very exciting!" agreed Dad.

Pray

Do you think Jesus is amazing? Do you know what things he can do?

Luke 8:22–25   29

Jesus helps a man

Mr Chang, at Lily's church, has a guide dog called Buster. Mr Chang cannot see so Buster leads Mr Chang into church and shows him where to sit. Then Buster sits quietly at Mr Chang's feet until they are ready to go. Lily thinks Buster is very clever.

Jesus met a man who was blind. His name was Bartimaeus. He didn't have a dog to help him. He used to sit by the road. One day, Bartimaeus heard lots of footsteps. "What's happening?" he asked.

Someone replied, "It's Jesus walking by."

Bartimaeus shouted, "Jesus, please help me!"

People around him said, "Ssshh, be quiet!"

Bartimaeus shouted even louder! Jesus called to him. "What do you want me to do?" he asked.

"I want to see," said Bartimaeus.

Jesus said, "I am happy to make you well."

And Bartimaeus could see!

Pray

Dear God, please help people who are blind and cannot see.

Mark 10:46–52

Thank you, God, for eyes!

What do you think Lily is doing? At pre-school one morning the children had to pretend they couldn't see. The teacher put blindfolds on them. Lily didn't like the blindfold so she just shut her eyes. They were given different things to feel. They had to guess what they were. Lily was given something very prickly.

"Ooh! It feels like a hedgehog! Oh, I know – it's a hairbrush."

Then they had to walk around the room with their eyes closed. One of the helpers led them by the hand.

"It was very hard," Lily told her mum afterwards. "I kept thinking I'd bump into things. I'm glad I can see!"

Lily went on, "Bartimaeus must have been so pleased when Jesus helped him see."

"Yes," agreed Mum. "His whole life changed. Just because Jesus took time to help him."

Pray

What do you like looking at? Tell God about it now.

"Thank you, God, for all the things I can see."

Mark 10:46–52

Music saves Jehoshaphat

On a Sunday morning, in Lily's church group, the children have a singing and music time. Each week the children are allowed to choose an instrument to play. Lily's favourite is the tambourine. When all the children are playing their instruments, it gets very noisy!

God loves it when we play music.

Jehoshaphat was a king in Jerusalem. He was very worried. Some large armies were coming to attack his country. How would they be able to fight them? He prayed to God. God told him, "Don't worry! I'll look after everyone."

Jehoshaphat called together some of his men. "I want you to march in front," he said, "and sing to God."

So they sang, "Praise the Lord! His love never ends!"

The soldiers of the enemy were surprised and confused. They ended up fighting each other!

Pray

Do you like making music? Say thank you to God for your favourite instrument.

2 Chronicles 20

Happy music

When you are feeling happy, what do you do? Laugh, sing, shout? Lily does all these things. And she likes to make music. Sometimes Lily's group play their musical instruments for the whole church. Lily makes happy, noisy sounds to say thank you to God.

One week Lily's brother Kai-Loong said, "Lily, you play far too loudly!"

But Dad said, "It sounds great to me – you always look as if you're having fun!"

God had told Jehoshaphat and his people that everything would be all right. When Jehoshaphat and his people realised that they did not have to fight, they were so happy. God had kept them safe. Do you know what they did? They played harps and blew trumpets. Lily thinks they probably played very loudly!

Pray

Find something that you can use to make music. Play it loudly and say, "Praise the Lord! His love never ends!"

Thank you, Lord!

Get moving with this action prayer.

For arms that swing and hands that clap,
Thank you Lord.

For feet that stamp and toes that tap,
   Thank you Lord.

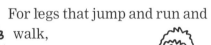

      For legs that jump and run and
      walk,
      Thank you Lord.

      For heads that nod
      and mouths that talk,
      Thank you Lord.

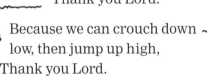

   Because we can crouch down
   low, then jump up high,
Thank you Lord.

   Because we can stand on tip-toe and reach
      for the sky,
         Thank you Lord.

For giving us bodies that bend
and stretch and move,
Thank you Lord.

Make a musical instrument to say thank you to God. Part-fill a
small plastic bottle with rice to make a shaker. Make sure the
lid is on tight.

Singalong

Lily loves to sing. When she and Mum are in the car, she always asks for music on. Then she joins in with all the songs.

At pre-school they do singing at the end of the morning. Lily's favourite song is "One, two, three, four, five, once I caught a fish alive!" Do you know that one? Lily sings it all the time! She likes singing songs about God too.

In the Bible there is a very famous person who made up his own songs. His name is David. He wrote songs which are called "psalms". Many of them are about how great God is. David sang about how God looked after him and how beautiful the world is. He loved the way God made the earth.

David sang to God, "Every good thing I have is a gift from you!"

Pray

Can you sing a song which tells God that you love him? Sing one you know or make up your own. God loves to hear you sing!

Singing to God

Lily was ready for bed. It was very dark outside. She opened her curtains and peeked through. She liked to see if she could find the moon. That night there were also lots of stars twinkling in the sky. She thought that God was very clever to make it all.

David thought so too. This is what one of his songs says, "The heavens keep telling the wonders of God, and the skies declare what he has done." David thought it was amazing that the sun came up every morning and shone so brightly in the sky. Following God made David so happy – it was the most important thing.

Praise the Lord!
Praise him with a loud voice!
Praise him with a quiet voice.
Praise him with a *singing* voice!
Praise him with every sound
you can make!

Pray

Be like David! Say, "Praise the Lord." Then say the words loudly, quietly, and sing them – and then say them while you make lots of noisy sounds!

Psalm 19

Dancing feet

It's Tuesday. What do you think Lily is going to do today?

"My ballet class – yippee!" she shouts. Today she is going to wear her brand new pink ballet shoes for the first time! Everyone who comes to the house has seen her new ballet shoes. After the class Lily says, "My shoes are lovely – they help me to skip much better. I love dancing!"

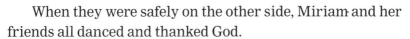

Miriam loved dancing too. She had a good reason to dance. Miriam and her family had been slaves in a country called Egypt. Then they had escaped. But they came to a big sea. How would they get across? God moved the water out of the way. The people walked on a dry pathway through the sea.

When they were safely on the other side, Miriam and her friends all danced and thanked God.

Pray

What do you like doing each week? Swimming? Ballet? Church?
Say, "Thank you, God, for..."

Exodus 15:19–21

A special book

Lily's mum has a very precious old book that belonged to her grandmother. It is full of lovely stories with beautiful pictures. The pages are very thin. Sometimes Lily and her mum get out the book and have a lovely time carefully turning the pages.

Josiah the king was unhappy. The temple where people went to worship God was in a terrible state. It was very dirty and some of the walls were broken down. Something had to be done. Josiah sent some workers to clean it up and repair it. Painters, carpenters and cleaners were all hard at work. One of the builders found a dusty wooden box. Inside was a kind of book – it was

very old. The book was all about how God wanted people to live. The builder took it to Josiah straight away.

Pray

Thank you, God, for the books I can read at the library, at home or at pre-school.

2 Kings 22 – 23

Best books

Do you have a favourite book? Every bedtime Lily chooses a
book for Mum or Dad to read. Her favourite is *Cinderella*.
Mum often says, "Do you really want me to read this *again*?"

"Yes, please," laughs Lily. "It's lovely!"

Lily enjoys other books too. They are all different – some
are happy, some are scary, some help her to learn her numbers
and letters, and some are stories from the Bible.

When King Josiah read the special book from the wooden

box, he knew he
was reading
God's words.
Josiah was
both happy
and sad. He
was happy
because
God's words
had been
found again.

That was wonderful. But he was sad because it meant that no
one had been reading God's book for many years. Josiah was
about to change that! He called everyone together and read to
them from God's book.

Pray

Can you tell God about your favourite
story from God's book, the Bible?

God knows all about me

Lily and Krista were playing with Lily's dolls. Krista had wrapped one in a blanket and was giving it a cuddle. "The baby in my mummy's tummy will be here soon," Krista said. "Then I'll have a real baby to cuddle."

Just then Lily's mum arrived with some juice and biscuits.

Lily was pleased. "I was just going to ask for a drink!" she laughed.

Mum smiled, "I know what you two are like!"

Here is another of David's songs from the Bible. David says, "God you are amazing. You love me when I am asleep and when I am awake. You even know the things I am going to do and say. Wherever I go, you will always be there to love me. Even before I was born you knew all about me. You knew what I would be like."

Pray

Thank you, God, that you made me and you know me so well.

Psalm 139

Playing together

Lily likes playing with girls, especially Krista. Usually she isn't so keen on boys. So she wasn't very happy when she knew Danny was coming over. "His games are stupid. He never wants to dress up!" she moaned.

When Danny arrived, Lily suggested playing "babies". Danny raced around with the doll's buggy. Lily's mum sent them into the garden.

Lily and Danny started playing in the sandpit. Danny filled Lily's watering can with water. They poured it into the sand and stirred it with a spade. Danny made rivers and dams. Lily helped. They had a lovely time getting into a big mess!

After Danny had gone home Lily said, "I liked having Danny here. We played different games."

"It's good that God made us all different," Mum agreed. "It would be very boring if everyone liked doing the same things."

Pray

Draw a picture of you playing your favourite game. Talk to God about it.

Psalm 139

Stephen the helper

Mr and Mrs Davis are friends of Lily's family. They go to the same church. One Sunday morning Mrs Davis gave Li-Lian a big bag of chocolate raisins.

"Thanks!" smiled Li-Lian.

"Share them with your sisters and brother," Mrs Davis told her.

But by the time Lily came out of her Sunday group, Li-Lian, Li-Ling and Kai-Loong had eaten nearly all the raisins!

Poor Lily. "It's not fair!" she said.

In the first church, in the Bible, people used to have meals together but some were complaining: "It's not fair! When the food is given out, we don't get our share."

So the leaders of the church said to Stephen, "We'd like you to be in charge of sharing out the food." Stephen made sure things were fair!

And guess what? Li-Lian bought Lily a little bag of chocolate raisins, just for her!

Pray

Dear God, please help me to be really helpful at home.

Helping and serving

Lily liked having juice and biscuits after church on a Sunday. Mr and Mrs Davis always served the drinks and then washed up. Lily started thinking about all the different people who helped in church. Some led the singing, some did the cleaning, while some helped lead the children's groups.

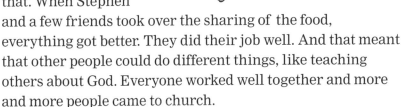

In the first church it was like that. When Stephen and a few friends took over the sharing of the food, everything got better. They did their job well. And that meant that other people could do different things, like teaching others about God. Everyone worked well together and more and more people came to church.

Lily asked her mum "What job could I do in church?"

Mum suggested, "You could collect up the songbooks after the service." So that's what Lily did each week.

Pray

Thank you, God, for all the different people who help me.

Acts 6:1–8

Paul and Silas in prison

Kai-Loong, Lily's brother, was in his Spiderman suit. Lily was a "baddie" and he was trying to put her in prison. She didn't really want to play and was glad when her dad walked through the door.

"Dad, why do you put people in prison?" asked Kai-Loong.

"Because they've done something they shouldn't, like stealing," Dad answered.

Paul was a friend of Jesus. He often ended up in prison, but not because he'd done something wrong. People didn't like him talking about Jesus and wanted to stop him. They thought putting him in prison would keep him out of the way. One time Paul and his friend Silas were in prison and their feet were chained up. Do you

think they were scared? Not Paul and Silas. They started singing! They knew God would be with them and help them.

Pray

Thank you, God, that you are always with us wherever we are.

Acts 16:16–40

Spot the difference

Paul and Silas are in prison.
Talk about what is happening in each picture.

Paul and Silas go free

Paul and Silas were singing to God in prison. Suddenly, there was a huge crash. The ground shook. The doors flew open and all the prisoners' chains fell off. The soldier in charge of the prison came rushing in. He was in big trouble – all the prisoners could have escaped! Paul shouted, "Don't worry – we're all here!" The soldier was amazed. He asked Paul and Silas if he too could become a friend of Jesus. A short time later Paul and Silas were allowed to go. They carried on telling people about Jesus, even though they might end up back in prison.

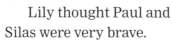

Lily thought Paul and Silas were very brave.

"They must have loved Jesus very much," she said.

"They did," said Dad. "They wanted everyone to know about Jesus and become friends of Jesus too."

Pray

Dear God, when I feel scared, help me to be brave.

Acts 16:16–40

A letter for Lily

Do you like getting letters? When does the post arrive at your house?

One day a letter arrived especially for Lily. It was from her grandparents in Hong Kong. Hong Kong is a very long way away and so Lily doesn't see them very often. The letter had a beautiful stamp with a flower on it. "Mum! I've got a letter from Gung Gung and Por Por! Can you read it to me?"

Paul, Jesus' friend, wrote lots of letters. His letters were to people in all the different churches. They didn't have posties in those days, so Paul used messengers to take his letters. They had to travel for many weeks to deliver them.

This is what Paul wrote to one church. "I thank God every time I think of you. Live happily together and show love for each other."

Pray

Thank you, God, for the letters and cards we receive and the people who deliver them.

Paul writes a special letter

At pre-school Lily was asked to paint a picture of her best friend. Can you guess who she chose? Krista! The teacher asked her why she liked Krista. Lily thought, "She's fun. We like playing the same things. She lets me play with her dolls and her dressing-up clothes."

Paul wrote a letter to a church about someone he liked very much. His name was Epaphroditus. The church had sent Epaphroditus to look after Paul and help him in his work.

Epaphroditus had been brilliant. But then he became very ill. Epaphroditus knew that his friends and family were worried about him, and he was sad. Paul wrote, "I am sending Epaphroditus back to you. Be sure to give him a really happy welcome. He deserves it. He has worked very hard!"

Pray

Who do you think is special? Say thank you to God for them.

"Thank you God for ..."

Philippians 2:25–30

Bad news!

Lily and Li-Lian were making "mixtures". They were behind the garage mixing soil, leaves, petals and water in an old glass jam jar. As Lily turned round, she knocked the jar over. It smashed on the ground. Glass went everywhere. They rushed to tell Mum the bad news.

"I'm glad you told me straight away – it's not always easy to tell the truth," Mum said.

Paul was in prison again for telling people about Jesus. He was not safe. Some men decided they wanted to kill Paul. Paul's nephew heard about it. He rushed to the prison to warn Paul. He then told the soldier in charge, "Don't let these men see my Uncle Paul! They plan to kill him!" Paul was moved away. He was safe because his nephew had been brave enough to tell the truth.

Pray

Dear God, please help me to tell the truth, even when it's scary.

Acts 23:11–24

Travelling around

Usually Lily and Mum walk to pre-school, but sometimes they go in the car. Lily's favourite way of travelling is on the bus. She likes sitting right at the back and looking out of the window. Lily travelled on an aeroplane to see her grandparents in Hong Kong. It was a very long journey and took hours. But she was only a baby so she doesn't really remember.

Paul did a lot of travelling. He went to lots of different towns, telling people about Jesus. Sometimes he walked, sometimes he rode on a horse or a camel, and quite often he went on ships. They weren't like big ferries. They were small sailing ships. You had to be brave to travel on them, as they weren't always very safe. But God kept Paul safe wherever he went.

Pray

Pretend you are sitting in a car, plane, bus or train. Say, "Thank you God for all the ways we can travel around."

Acts 27:1 – 28:15

First steps in Bible reading

The *Tiddlywinks* range of Little Books

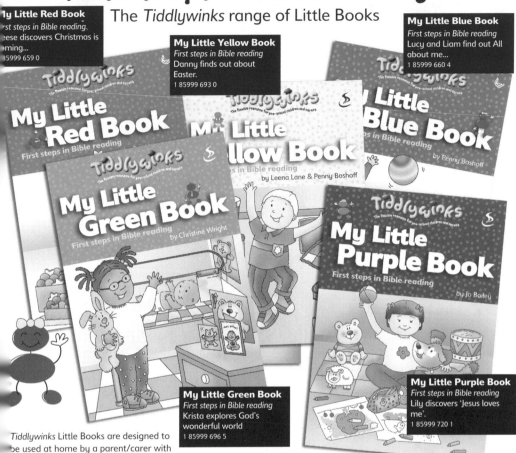

My Little Red Book
First steps in Bible reading.
Reese discovers Christmas is coming...
1 85999 659 0

My Little Yellow Book
First steps in Bible reading
Danny finds out about Easter.
1 85999 693 0

My Little Blue Book
First steps in Bible reading
Lucy and Liam find out All about me...
1 85999 660 4

My Little Green Book
First steps in Bible reading
Krista explores God's wonderful world
1 85999 696 5

My Little Purple Book
First steps in Bible reading
Lily discovers 'Jesus loves me'.
1 85999 720 1

Tiddlywinks Little Books are designed to be used at home by a parent/carer with an individual child. Linked to the themes covered in the *Tiddlywinks* Big Books, children can discover and learn about the Bible and share their discoveries with you. There are 50 first steps in Bible reading pages in each book, with a story for each day and extra activity pages of fun things to do. Children will love exploring the Bible with child characters Lucy and Liam, Reese, Danny, Krista and Lily.
A5, 64pp £3.50 each (Prices subject to change)

You can order these or any other *Tiddlywinks* resources from:
- Your local Christian bookstore
- Scripture Union Mail Order:
  Telephone 01908 856006
- Online: log on to
  www.scriptureunion.org.uk/tiddlywinks
  to order securely from our online bookshop

COMING SOON
My Little Orange Book

> *When the Big Books are used in conjunction with the Little Books, children and adults encounter an attractive mixture of stories and activities that will encourage everybody to know and trust in Jesus.*
> **Diana Turner,**
> **Editor of Playleader Magazine**

The flexible resource for pre-school children and carers

Also now on sale!
Glitter and Glue. Pray and Play.
Even more craft and prayer ideas for use with under fives

The boat sinks!

Lily and Kai-Loong were having a great time in the bath. They had emptied all the toys into the water. One of the toys was a plastic boat. They put in the little people. They filled a cup and poured more and more water into the boat. Can you guess what happened? The boat tipped over and all the people fell out!

One day, Paul was travelling in a ship. It sailed right into a storm. It was pouring with rain and the wind was howling.

All the sailors were very scared as the ship was tossed in the waves. Paul stood up and shouted, "Don't be afraid. God will look after us." The ship got stuck on a rock. The captain yelled, "Everyone jump in and swim for shore." They all made it safely, just as Paul had said they would.

Pray

Dear God, please help anyone who is feeling scared at the moment.

Solomon plans the temple

Lily's family were planning to have some more rooms built onto their house. Mum and Dad called it an "extension". At the moment Lily shared a room with Li-Lian, but soon she would have her own room.

"When will my room be ready, Mum?" Lily asked.

"It takes a long time to build an extension," Mum answered. "The builders have to draw plans and buy all the materials before they can even start."

Solomon had been king for four years. He wanted to build a temple, a special house for God. He made careful plans. He wanted all the best materials. The best wood came from another country far away. Solomon made friends with the king of that country and asked if they could have some of their trees. The trees were chopped down and sent to Solomon.

Pray

Do you go to a special building to worship God? Do you talk to God at home? You can talk to God now!

1 Kings 5:1–12

Wood and more wood . . .

"Where does wood come from?" Lily was looking at the kitchen table.

"It comes from trees," Mum replied. "We've got all sorts of things in our house that are made out of wood. Why don't you see what you can find?"

Lily found bowls, doors, toys, and shelves that were all made from wood. Li-Ling showed her the sawdust in the guinea-pig cage – even that comes from wood!

Solomon was delighted when the wood arrived for God's temple. The walls were going to have wood from floor to ceiling. Then on the wood, special craftsmen would carve animals, trees and flowers. Solomon wanted the very best of everything for God's special house.

Next time you see a tree, remember all the things that are made from wood.

Pray

Find something made out of wood to hold. Say, "Thank you, God, for trees and for all the things that can be made from wood."

1 Kings 5:1–12

The building begins

Lily watched in excitement as the builders got to work. First they dug a trench. "They're digging the foundations," said Mum. The builders poured in concrete and waited for it to go hard. They started laying bricks. The rows of bricks grew higher and higher. In went a new door and some windows. Lily was going to have two windows in her room.

Work had begun on God's temple. There were two main rooms. There was a big rectangular room, and when you went inside there was a smaller square room. There was a double door between them. God told Solomon, "If you promise to follow me, I will live among your people in this temple." Solomon hurried to get the temple finished.

Pray

Thank you, God, for the building I live in – thank you that it keeps me safe and warm.

Building with bricks

Lily and Kai-Loong were playing with the bricks. Lily had the wooden blocks and Kai-Loong had the Duplo.

"Let's see who can build the tallest tower," Kai-Loong suggested.

He put his pieces on the base and started fixing them together. Lily was much quicker – she had soon made a tall tower.

"I've won!" she shouted. But as she said it, her tall tower toppled over. All the bricks crashed everywhere.

Mum came in. "I'm glad you're not building our extension," she laughed.

The builders of the temple must have been very clever. They didn't have machines to help them. They did everything by hand. They held their tools to cut the stones into the right shape. Then they carried them into the temple. There was no hammering inside. Solomon wanted the temple to be quiet.

Pray

Thank you, God, for builders who build our homes, roads and shops.

1 Kings 6:1–14

Lily's making page

Make a card for someone you know who is ill – deliver it to them yourself or put it in the postbox.

Make a boat out of a small plastic tub. Use a straw for a mast and make a sail out of paper. Does it float?

Choosing decorations

The building work was done. The extension was finished. Lily and her mum were going shopping. They were going to choose new curtains and paint for the walls. Lily's favourite colour is purple. There was going to be a purple carpet in her room. For her birthday she had already been given a purple

cushion with a fairy on it and a beautiful lamp. "I can't wait to move into my new room," smiled Lily.

Solomon was planning the decoration of God's temple. The wooden walls were beautifully carved.

"It needs more," Solomon said. "Cover the inside room with pure gold. Let's even have gold chains across the front."

That was not all. A famous craftsman came and made two bronze pillars. They were put at the door to the temple. It was all bright and shiny.

Pray

Think of your favourite room. Tell God why it is special.

The temple is finished

Lily was worried. She had been playing with Mum's jewellery. There was a lovely shiny gold necklace. Lily had put it on. But then she forgot she was wearing it. And now she had lost it. Lily knew Mum would be cross. And she was!

"Lily! I've told you before – you mustn't play with my things! That gold necklace is very valuable."

They looked everywhere. At last they found it. It had caught in Lily's T-shirt when she changed her clothes.

Lily had seen a picture of Solomon's temple in a book. It did look very beautiful. "If all the walls were covered in gold it must have been very expensive!" she thought.

Solomon worked for seven years to build the temple. He looks pleased to have finished it, doesn't he? Solomon loved God so much that he wanted to give God the best.

Pray

Thank you, God, that Solomon tried his best for you. Help me to try my best.

1 Kings 6:15–38

Selling and buying

Lily and her mum are at the curtain shop to choose Lily's curtains. There are so many different fabrics to choose from – colours and patterns, flowers and pictures, rabbits and racing cars . . .

Lily doesn't know which to choose. At last, she spots some purple material – it has white dots all over it. "This is my favourite. It will go with my carpet."

Paul met someone who sold material. Her name was Lydia and she had come to Philippi to sell expensive purple cloth. Lydia liked to go down to the river to pray with some of the other women. Paul went there to pray too. He told her how special Jesus was. Lydia and her family became friends of Jesus. Lydia begged Paul, "Please come and stay with us and tell us more about Jesus!"

Pray

What are you wearing today? Say thank you to God for each thing you are wearing and for the people who make our clothes.

Lights to give light

Lily's brother Kai-Loong was doing a project about light at school. He had to find pictures of everything that gave out light. Lily was helping him look through some magazines. They found torches, streetlights, car headlights and table lamps. "Lights help us see the way in the dark," Kai-Loong said importantly.

Can you think of anything else that gives out light? Look

around your house and see what you can find.

Jesus talked about light. He said, "No one lights a lamp and puts it under a bowl or under a bed. A lamp is always put on a lampstand, so that people who come into a house will see the light." Lily thought this made sense – if it's dark in the house then you turn the light on!

Pray

Thank you, God, for all the different lights we have.

Luke 8:16

Let your light shine

Lily thought about lights helping us to see in the dark. Jesus said we should be like lights. Lily wondered what he meant. She remembered all the stories she'd heard about Jesus and his friends. They were brave, kind and generous. Lily asked Jesus, "Please help me to be like the people I hear about in the Bible."

The light made Lily feel safe. She was snuggled up in bed. Lily was a bit scared when it was really dark. The light shining was her new lamp. It was in the shape of a little house and had a family of rabbits inside. Lily looked around her new room. Her mum had stuck some stars on to the ceiling – they glowed as Lily watched them.

"Dear Jesus," whispered Lily, "please help me to shine out your love to everyone!"

Pray

Thank you, Jesus, for the way you love and care for everyone. Help me to be like you.

Luke 8:16

First steps in dealing with anger

The child's clenched fists battered against the door and the tears streamed down his flaming cheeks. Angry? Oh yes! We can all recognise an angry child when we see one.

Young children are so open and honest about their emotions. As adults, we wholeheartedly enjoy the spontaneous expression of our children's joy and love. Yet we find it much more difficult to handle less comfortable emotions that are expressed with the same vigour.

You may be asking, "Isn't it wrong to be angry?" The Bible states: "In your anger do not sin." In other words, it is not the anger that is the problem but what we do with it that counts. Yet how are our children supposed to learn to deal with their anger in an effective way, if our responses are: "Don't answer me back"; "Don't look at me like that"; "Stop that shouting." If we want to help our children learn to handle their anger effectively, we need to set the example and give them the opportunities to learn how to manage their own anger.

We might find it easier to deal with this emotion if we consider its purpose. Anger is like a warning light on the dashboard of the car, indicating, "Something is not OK for me. I need change."

It takes a great deal of skill and patience from parents and carers to help our children identify what the actual issues are that are causing their feelings of anger and to learn to express this in a constructive rather than destructive way. That's one of the greatest challenges of parenting and nurturing the children God has given into our care!

Have you enjoyed this book?

Then take a look at the other Big Books in the *Tiddlywinks* range. Why not try them all?

The Big Purple Book
Themes: Jesus loves me; God loves it when I... make music, sing, dance, look at books, I'm 'me'; Friends and followers; Materials and technology
1 85999 719 8

The Big Red Book
Themes: Christmas is coming; People we meet; Stories Jesus told; God gives us food
1 85999 658 2

The Big Blue Book
Themes: All about me; God gives us... homes, clothes, food, etc; People who knew Jesus; Friends of God
1 85999 657 4

'I love this! It's great!'
Sarah, leader of a 3 to 5s group in Victoria, Australia.

Tiddlywinks Big Books are designed for use in any pre-school setting. The multi-purpose outlines are packed full of play, prayers, crafts, stories and rhymes; simply pick and mix ideas to meet the particular needs of your group. You'll find plenty of practical advice on setting up and running a pre-school group, plus ideas in every session to help you include adult carers. The children will love the illustrated activity pages.
A4, 96pp, £8.99 each (Prices subject to change)

You can order these or any other *Tiddlywinks* resources from:

● Your local Christian bookstore
● Scripture Union Mail Order: Telephone 01908 856006
● Online: log on to **www.scriptureunion.org.uk/tiddlywinks** to order securely from our online bookshop

25 multi-purpose outlines for pre-school groups
● God gives us families
● Friends of Jesus
● What's the weather like?
Feature series:
● **Easter**

The Big Green Book
Themes: God's wonderful world; God gives us people Let's find out about Jesus; God knows when I'm... happy, cross, sad, scared, busy
1 85999 695 7

The Big Yellow Book
Themes: Easter; God gives us families; Friends of Jesus; What's the weather like?
1 85999 692 2

'...really pleased with your material and look forward integrating Tiddlywinks into our existing programme.'
Marion, Scotland

Tiddlywinks
The flexible resource for pre-school children and carers

Also now on sale
Glitter and Glue. Pray and Play
Even more craft and prayer ideas for use with under fives